All songs arranged by Tom Roed except those listed with *

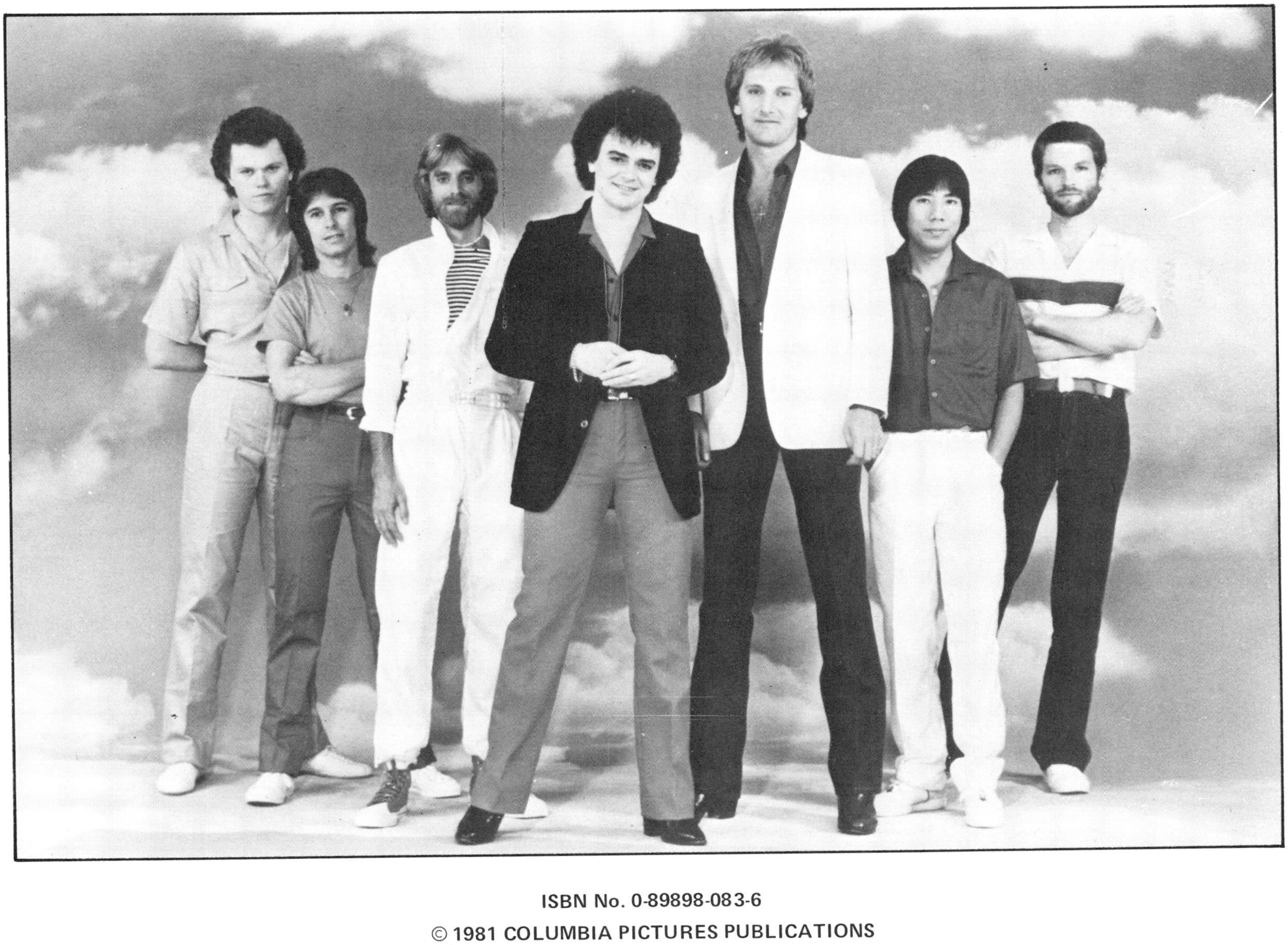

ALBUM COVERS

ISBN No. 0-89898-083-6

Editor: Audrey L. Kleiner / Production: Frank J. Hackinson / Printer: Central Litho (Miami)

LOST IN LOVE

Moderately ♩=120

Words and Music by
GRAHAM RUSSELL

G(add 9)
G
C6
Am7
I re - al - ize the best part of love is the thin -
2.7. (see additional lyrics) 6. (Instr. solo)
p
mp

Cmaj9
C6
Cmaj9
C6
nest slice, and it don't count for much but I'm not
Am9
Am7
Am9
Am7
let - ting go, I be - lieve there's too much to be - lieve
1.3.5.7.8. etc.
2.4.6.
G(add 9)
G
G(add 9)
G
in.
2.4. So,

Verses 2 & 4:
So, lift your eyes if you feel you can,
Reach for a star and I'll show you a plan.
I've figured it out, what I needed was someone to show me.
(To Chorus:)

Verses 3. 5. 7. 8. etc.
Lost in love and I don't know much,
Was I thinking aloud and fell out of touch?
But I'm back on my feet, and eager to be what you wanted.

EVERY WOMAN IN THE WORLD

Words and Music by
DOMINIC BUGATTI and
FRANK MUSKER

Cm7
Cm7/F
Dm7
Gm7
Laugh - ing my - self to sleep, wak - ing up lone - ly. I
danc - in' in the dark with stran - gers, no love a - round me. When
Cm7
Cm7/B♭
1. Cm7/F
2. Cm7/F
need - ed some - one to hold me, oh. It's such a Girl, you're
sud - den - ly you found me, oh.
B♭maj7
B♭maj7/D
E♭maj7
Cm7
ev - 'ry wom - an in the world to me. You're my fan - ta - sy, you're
Cm7/F
B♭maj7
B♭maj7/D
E♭maj7
Dm7
my re - al - i - ty. Girl, you're ev - 'ry wom - an in the world to me. You're

Cm7
D7sus4
D7
G
ev - 'ry - thing I need, you're ev - 'ry - thing to me, oh girl.
C
G
C♯m7/F♯
B
Emaj7
Ev - 'ry - thing good, ev - 'ry - thing fine, that's what you are. So, put your
B
Emaj7
hand in mine and to - geth - er we'll climb as high as the high - est star. I'm liv - in' a life -

C♯m7
C♯m7/F♯
D♯m7
G♯m7
C♯m7
C♯m7/B
— time in ev - 'ry min - ute that we're to - geth - er, — and I'm stay - in' right here for - ev - er, oh. —
F♯/A♯
Bmaj7
Bmaj7/D♯
Emaj7
— Girl, you're ev - 'ry wom - an in the world to me.
C♯m7
C♯m7/F♯
Bmaj7
Bmaj7/D♯
You're my fan - ta - sy, — you're my re - al - i - ty. Girl, you're ev - 'ry wom - an in the world to
Emaj7
D♯m7
C♯m7
D♯7sus4
D♯7
me. You're ev - 'ry - thing — I need, — you're ev - 'ry - thing — to me, — oh girl. —

G♯
4 fr.
C♯
Dm7/G
Girl, you're
Repeat and fade
Cmaj7
Cmaj7/E
Fmaj7
Dm7
ev - 'ry wom - an in the world to me.
You're my fan - ta - sy, you're
Dm7/G
Cmaj7
Cmaj7/E
Fmaj7
Em7
my re - al - i - ty. Girl, you're ev - 'ry wom - an in the world to me.
You're
Dm7
Dm7/G
ev - 'ry - thing I need, you're ev - 'ry - thing to me. Girl, you're

THE ONE THAT YOU LOVE

Words and Music by
GRAHAM RUSSELL

Moderately ♩ = 104
C
C
1. Now the night has gone;
2. Don't say the morn-ing's come;
3. (see additional lyrics)
p
mf
mp
espr.
Gm
now the night has gone a - way;
don't say the morn-ing's come so soon.
C
Gm
does - n't seem that long; we hard - ly had two words to say.
Must we end this way, when so much here is hard to lose?

Dm
Hold me in your arms for just an -
Love is ev - 'ry - where; I
Bm7-5
C
Gm6/Bb
A7/C#
oth - er day, I prom-ise this one will go slow; oh,
know it is; such mo-ments as this are too few; oh,
Dm
Dm/C
G
we have the right you know;
it's all up to you;
Dm
Dm/C
we have the right you
it's all up to
1.
G
know.
2.3.
G
you.
G/F
Here I

Chorus:
C
G/C
F/C
G/C
am, the one that you love, asking for an - oth - er day; un - der-
C
G/C
F/C
stand, the one that you love, loves you in so man - y ways.
1.
G/C
F/C
D.S.
2.
G/C
3.
G/C
Here I
A/C♯
Dm
Dm/C
The night has gone, a part of yes - ter - day;

Verse 3:
Tell me we can stay;
Tell me we can stay, oh please.
They are the words to say,
The only words I can believe.
Hold me in your arms for just another day,
I promise this one will go slow; oh,
We have the right you know;
We have the right you know.
(To Chorus:)

I'VE GOT YOUR LOVE

Words and Music by
GRAHAM RUSSELL

Fmaj7
F/G
G
C
I've got your love;
Bb6
Dm
Am
I don't know why you hid it.
it's such a to - tal feel - ing.
mf
Bm7-5
Am
Am/G
Fmaj7
I've nev - er felt like this be - fore.
I don't know where it all be - gan.
F/G
G
Fmaj7
G/F
"I won't fall in love;"
mp

Fmaj7
G/F
Am
you said it so sure. You have-n't no-
C
Dm
1. G/F
ticed you nev - er say that an - y - more.
C
Bb6
Dm
I've got your love, and it's a per -
Am/C
Bm7-5
Am
Am/G
fect rea - son for un - der - stand - ing life some more.

Fmaj7
G/F
Fmaj7
You burnt your fin - gers be - fore,
G/F
Fmaj7
G/F
G
D.S.
burnt your fin - gers be - fore.
2.
G/F
Eb
Db6
I've got your love,
mf
Fm
Cm/Eb
Dm7-5
and if I lose all oth - ers
I know it would-

Cm
Cm/B♭
A♭
B♭/A♭
B♭
- n't hurt at all.
E♭
D♭6
Fm
I've got your love;
I don't know how
Cm/E♭
Dm7-5
we did it.
I don't know why
Cm
Cm/B♭
A♭
B♭/A♭
B♭
it seemed so long.

F♯
E6
I've got your love,
G♯m
D♯m
I've got your love,
E♯m7-5
D♯m
D♯/C♯
I don't know why it seemed so long.
Bmaj7
C♯/B
C♯
Repeat and fade

TONITE

Words and Music by
GRAHAM RUSSELL

Moderately, with a 2 feel
F
C/E
B♭
F
C/E
B♭
F
C/E
1. Now you tell me that the time is right, you've
2. (See additional lyrics)

Dm
Dm/C
B♭
let your feel - ings go;
and you know I won't
C
F
F/C
C
use them up too fast.
F
C/E
Dm
I can't prom-ise you the best there is but, ooh, I'm gon - na try.
Dm/C
B♭
C
I'm nev-er gon - na let you go to - night.

F
C/E
Dm
To - nite, the
mf
Am
start of a love to re-mem - ber.
To -
Dm
nite, a love that will nev - er be
1. Gm
C
F
E♭
B♭/D
end - ed.
To - nite,
f

F
E♭
B♭/D
D.S. 𝄋
to - nite.
2.3.
Gm
C
end - ed.
To -
(Instrumental Solo 4th time)
4.
Gm
C
To -
(End Solo)
F
E♭
B♭/D
nite,
to - nite.
F
E♭
B♭/D
f
B♭
B♭/C
How man - y times has love fall - en through
mp

F
Eb
Bb
when I left it all up to you? I took your words
Bb/C
Dm
Dm/C
when you said it's got to be just right. I
Gm
Bb/C
C7
need you now, I need you now.
grad. cresc.
C/D
D
Em
To - nite, the start of a love to re - mem -
f

Verse 2: Let me take you where there's no return;
Where dreams can all come true.
I've got the feeling we've been holding on;
What we're feeling is ours alone.
No one will ever know
Just how we feel about tonite.

(Chorus:)

I CAN'T GET EXCITED

Words and Music by
GRAHAM RUSSELL

Cm
You say you'll love me a - gain.
try - ing just to make you see;
F
I can't say what I can - not do. It's
hop - ing I might be the one. So
B♭
been too long with - out some - one. How
calm down, love, it will be all right. The
B♭/A♭
could you let me sink this far a - way
time to bring back love is not to - night.

Cm
— from you? — Now — you're here, —
— I nev - er thought I'd have to say — that
F
won - d'ring why — you can't — get near. — I
you should leave — and go — a - way. —
Bb
Eb/Bb
Bb
Bb/Ab
can't get ex - cit - ed. Can't — get ex - cit - ed.
f
Eb/Ab
Bb/Ab
Eb
There's a thou - sand things — to do; —
You can see me look — right through; -

Cm7
1.3. F
2. F
D.C.
I can't do — an - y - thing — with — you. — I — to — do. —
I don't feel — like I used —
4. F
Cm
Ab
— to — do. —
mf
Not in love; —
still not in love — with you; — not in love. —
I'm still not in love — with you; — not in —

A♭
Cm
love.
Still not in love with you;
A♭
To Coda
not in love.
E♭
F
Tell me why you can't leave me lone - ly.
Tell me why I'm
Gm
F
E♭
tak - ing a chance on you;

Gm
F
E♭
play 3 times
8va
taking a chance on you;
8va
D.S. al Coda
Coda
A♭
E♭
A♭/E♭
E♭
Can't get ex-cit-ed. I
E♭/D♭
A♭/D♭
E♭/D♭
A♭
can't get ex-cit-ed
You can see me look
There's a thou-sand things
Fm
B♭
Repeat and fade
right through;
to do;
I don't feel like I used to do.
I can't do an-y-thing with you.
Can't

AMERICAN HEARTS

Words and Music by
DOMINIC BUGATTI and
FRANK MUSKER

Cm
F
B♭
chil - dren of their time, wo - wo. — They
doc - tor gives her pills, wo - wo. —
E♭
lived in a world — that was cold — and un - car - ing. They
Who are these stran - gers who used — to be lo - vers?
3. (See additional lyrics)
A♭
swore they would change — it with lov - ing and shar - ing.
Now they've got noth - ing to say — to each oth - er.
E♭
A♭/E♭
E♭
They nev - er lived — like their par - ents had done. — Their
Too far a - part — to dis - cuss — their mis - takes. — They

in - no - cence shone — like the sun. —
fought with di - vorce, — and it breaks — their
A - mer - i can hearts, —
Bb
Eb/Bb
Bb
Eb/Bb
Bb
Eb/Bb
Bb
so filled with e -
Eb
mo - tion. —
A - mer - i - can hearts, —
Bb
Eb/Bb
Bb
Eb/Bb
Bb
Eb/Bb
Bb
Eb
so eas - i - ly bro - ken. —
1.
Cm
F
D.S.
Now —
f
mf

3. Now that it's over, they each go on living;
Never forgetting but somehow forgiving.
They'll care for their children;
Protect them with pride;
And that's how the dream will survive in
American hearts. . .

KEEPING THE LOVE ALIVE

Words and Music by
RICHARD SUPA

F/C C | 1. F/G G F/G G | 2.3. F/G G F/G G

in the end. We
walk a - way.

Chorus:

Cadd 2 C Cadd 2 C

can't stop, the feel - ing's too strong.

f

F F/G G F/G G C

We've got the will to hang on. Can't stop; we

Am Dm C/E

strug - gle and fight to sur - vive; just

1.
F
F/G
G
Cadd2
C
Amadd2
Am
keep-ing the love a - live.
mf
Fadd2
F
F/G
G
D.S.
2.
F
F/G
G
keep -ing the love a - live.
Bb
F/A
Ab
If we
Eb/G
Ab/Bb
Bb
stand the test of time love will be the last - ing kind. We

3. We try to forget the past
So many times.
It's hard to make those memories leave.
With all we have at stake,
We'll bend until we break,
'Cause we both believe.

(Repeat Chorus:)

HAVING YOU NEAR ME

Words and Music by
GRAHAM RUSSELL

C
G
F
role I us - ual - ly play. Don't speak too
deep our love could be. To - night we'll
G
Em7
Am
much of what's been go - ing on; the
touch un - til it's time to go, then I'm
F
G
Em7
past is o - ver and gone. Give me your trou - bled mind,
leav - ing it up to you. E - ven a fool would know
3. (Instrumental Solo ad lib.)
Am
C/G
F
you know it's due. I can do so much for
that I'm not through, I can do so much for

Chorus:
F/G
C
you; —
you; —
I want you.
I want you.
Hav - ing you near — me
End Solo
Em7
hold - ing you near — me; —
Bdim
Am
G
Fmaj7
I want you to stay and nev - er go a - way.
F/G
C
It's so — right; hav - ing you near — me, —

Em7
Bdim
hold- ing you near me;
I'll love you to -
Am
G
Fmaj7
G
night, it feels so right,
feels so
mp
1. C
right.
2. C
right.
D.S.
3. C
right.
rit.

THIS HEART BELONGS TO ME

Words and Music by
GRAHAM RUSSELL

D/C
Bm
when they're a - fraid to say, "I want
you to hold on to me"?
D
C
If I let you go a - gain to - night,
D/C
Bm
whose arms will keep me warm and take

D
F♯m
G
F♯m
G
me where I long to be?
But if I lose and then surren-
der all I know,
what would I do
if you de-cid-ed to let go?
mf

Em
D
C
Hope-less - ly I'd stand there with ev - 'ry-thing all gone;
Bm
A7
A/C♯
my head down in my hands, won - der - ing
D
Dsus
D
Em
why. This heart be - longs to me
(Instrumental Solo 4th time)
f
Em/D
and knows what I be-lieve; but now

C
Dsus
it longs to be on - ly with you.
1.
D
D.S.
2.4.5.6. etc.
D
Repeat and fade
This heart
3.
D
Em
C
D
Em
My love goes on-ly to one; this heart be-longs to me.
ff
C
My love goes on - ly to one; this

D
Em
C
heart be-longs to me.
My love,
D
Em
D.S.S.
my love; this heart be- longs to me.
f

Verse 2:

Where are all the words I sometimes say
When I'm afraid to ask,
"I want you to hold on to me"?
Anyway you want to let me know
You're sharing my belief
Of wanting to hold on to me.
I tell the truth and risk you running from my life;
So much to lose; I guess
You know how hard I try.

I'LL NEVER GET ENOUGH OF YOU

Words by JEANNE NAPOLI

Music by
GARY PORTNOY and
JUDY QUAY

Moderately Slow
expressively
p
E
mp
1. All last night we lay in bed
2. nev - er had to say a word; it was
3. 4. (See additional lyrics)
5. (Instrumental Solo)

F#m
A
mak - ing love.
all right there.
I nev - er felt so much
The warmth in - side us flamed,
E
1.3.
be - fore with an - y - one.
and cir - cled ev - 'ry - where.
We
2.4.5.
B/D#
C#m
G#m
And if I nev - er have an - oth - er love, well, at
mf
A
E
B/D#
C#m
least I had last night.
Now I know how the feel -

G♯m
1.2.
A
ing grows 'cause you made me come a - live.
A/B
E
I'll nev - er get e - nough; nev - er get e - nough;
f
F♯m
A/B
E
nev- er get e - nough of you. Nev - er get e - nough;
F♯m
nev - er get e - nough; nev - er get e - nough

A/B
Amaj7
of you.
I only want to give
E
you more.
Amaj7
Am
D.S. 𝄋
3.
A
made me come;
B♭
B♭/C
made me come a - live.
I'll
mf

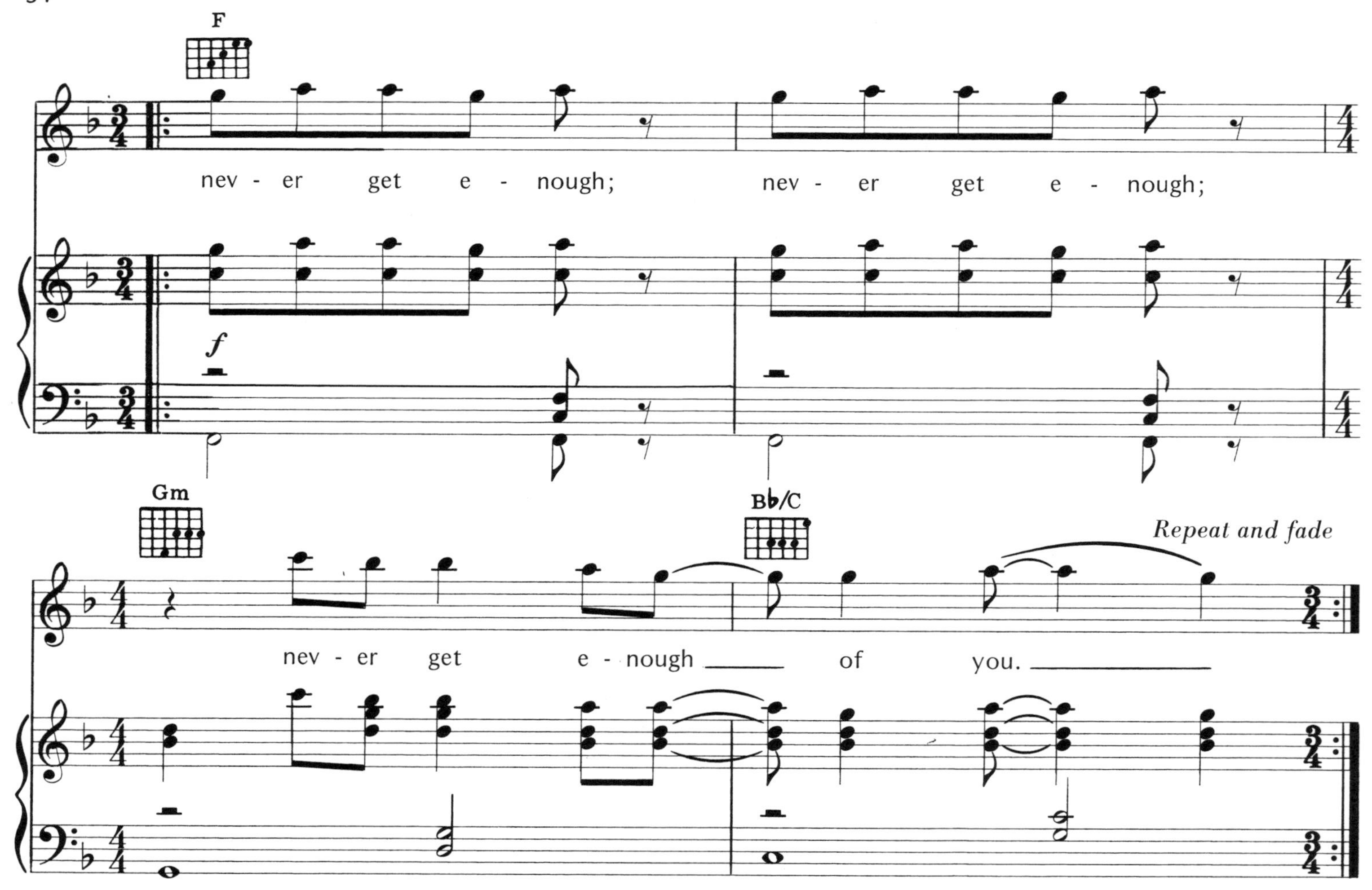

3. Now you're gone; I'm all alone,
   Just lying here.
   Waiting for the moment when I'll feel you near.

4. I never asked if you'd come back;
   I'm too damn proud.
   I just smiled and touched your hair as you went out.

OLD HABITS DIE HARD

Words and Music by
CRISTON BARKER and
DAVID MOYSE

C
G
with you, 'cause you're one bad hab - it that I
C
G/B
Am7
D7
can't re - fuse..
Old hab - its die hard,
f
G
C
G
old hab - its die hard.
1. C
2. C
G
Old hab - its die hard,

C
G
C
old hab - its die hard.
Em
Bm
You know and I know that you can't live on
mf
C
G
Em
mem - o - ries a - lone.
There's just one mem - 'ry that I'm
Bm
C
think - ing of,
just one hab - it that I

D7
G
can't shake off; it's you!
Old hab-its die hard,
f
C
G
C
old hab-its die hard,
G
C
To Coda
G
old hab-its die hard,
old hab-its die hard.
C
G
C
And I know that I'm still in love with you, 'cause you're
mf

G
C
Am7
one bad hab - it that I
can't re - fuse.
D7
D.S. al Coda
Coda
G
And there's
old hab - its die hard,
C
G
C
old hab - its die hard,
G
C
Bm
Am
D7sus
G
old hab - its die hard.

ALL OUT OF LOVE

Words and Music by
GRAHAM RUSSELL

1.3.
2.4.
E/G♯
Emaj7
F♯7sus
Emaj7
ment-ed and torn a-part. 2. I doesn't real-
F♯7sus
F♯
Chorus:
B
F♯/A♯
ly know. I'm all out of love, I'm so lost with-out you, I
all out of love, what am I with-out you? I
mf
E/G♯
to Coda
1.3.5.6.7.8.9.
E
F♯
know you were right, be-liev- ing for so long. I'm
can't be too late to say
(6. 8.) I know I was so wrong. I'm
2.4.
E
F♯
B
1.
D.S.
that I was so wrong. 3. I

2.
F♯/A♯
G♯m
D♯m
Ooh, what are you think - ing of?
E
D♯m
C♯m
G♯m
What are you think - ing of?
D♯m
E
D♯m
C♯m
What are you think - ing of?
What are you think - ing of?
E
F♯/G♯
F♯/A♯
D.S.S. through 9th ending al Coda
I'm
a tempo
rit.

Verse 2:
I wish I could carry your smile in my heart,
For times when my life seems so low.
It would make me believe what tomorrow could bring,
When today doesn't really know, doesn't really know.
I'm . . . (To Chorus:)

Verse 3:
I want you to come back and carry me home,
Away from these long, lonely nights.
I'm reaching for you. Are you feeling it too?
Does the feeling seem oh, so right?

Verse 4:
And what would you say if I called on you now,
And said that I can't hold on?
There's no easy way, it gets harder each day,
Please love me or I'll be gone, I'll be gone.
I'm . . . (To Chorus:)

DON'T TURN ME AWAY

Words and Music by
GRAHAM RUSSELL

Moderately
F
C/E
Dm
C6
f
Bb
C
F
C
C/A
C/G
ff
f
F
C/E
Dm
1. We shared such a spe - cial love; It seemed to have no end;
2. (See additional lyrics)
mf
C6
Bb
C
but now it hurts me just to re - mem -

F
C
C/A
C/G
F
ber.
Your eyes used to
f
mf
C/E
Dm
C6
tell me so much that words could nev - er find;
B♭
C
Gm
3
and now you say
you don't know where your fu - ture lies;
Gm/F
E♭
Csus
but you've got to find it now or get left be - hind.

Chorus:
F
C/E
Dm
Don't turn me a - way; I can't for - get it all in just one day.
f
C6
B♭
C
Take some time to speak your mind but say it's not o -
F
C
C/A
C/G
F
ver.
Don't turn me a - way;
f
C/E
Dm
C6
B♭
don't close the door on us this way.
I'm so sure

C
F
that there's much more, you just have to tell me.
1. C
C/A
C/G
2. F
F/E♭
F/D
Cm
And just when you need-
mf
Cm/B♭
B♭
F
ed me, I said, "I'd be there un - til the end."
Cm
Cm/B♭
B♭
What is it that's changed in you, when all I want is to

C
Csus
C
be your friend?
I need a friend.
ff
Don't turn me a - way,
don't
F
C/E
p
gradual cresc.
Dm
C6
B♭
turn me a - way,
don't turn me a - way.
1.2.3.4.
5.
C
C
F
Don't
f

Verse 2: Remember those fireside nights;
It's not that long ago.
You said you wanted to stay there forever.
I gave you the strength of my hand
When things were running low.
I didn't know you would go back on what you said.
There must be some reasons there
That you don't want to share.

(Chorus:)

JUST ANOTHER WOMAN

Words and Music by
GRAHAM RUSSELL

Rock with a steady beat

1.2.4.
To next strain
2. As
3.5.6. etc.
Repeat and Fade
Just 1. Knock up - on my win - dow
2. See additional lyrics
3. Instrumental Solo - ad lib.
late at night; mak - ing me be - lieve that some -
Eb
thing's not right. I look through the win - dow but all
Bb

Fm7
Eb
Bb
I can see is the rain.
Stand - ing on my door - step, not ve - ry old;
look - ing so help - less and look - ing so cold;
a wom - an who need - ed some help; now she's lost her way.

2. As we sat by the fire, the flames just grew;
Talking about different things we knew.
Watching a new day arrive, right inside my room.
The more I listened the more she told;
Weaving in and out of my mind with a skill unknown.
She was tall. . .

MY BEST FRIEND

Words and Music by
GRAHAM RUSSELL

G
Bm7
Am
laugh hard at the world, I know;
Bm7
Em
G/D
now that the sea - sons show
you tell me, love, your heart
f
mf
C
D
G
F/G
will soon mend.
mp
Am
Bm
D
We count-ed ev - 'ry day
on - ly to show we need -
Instrumental Solo 2nd time
mf

Am
Bm7
ed each oth - er.
Who needs a rea - son to love when
Em7
Em/D
C
D
friends just seem to know; they know it.
End Solo.
G
Bm7
You have lots of dreams, I know;
mp
Am
Bm7
now it's the close of the show.
f

Em
G/D
C
Let's hope it all passes by in the
end. So get yourself along, you're my best friend.
1. G
Dm/G
D.S.
2. G
mf
mp
Bm
Am
G
rit.
p

HERE I AM

Words and Music by
NORMAN SALLITT

Dm7
those thoughts of you keep taunt - ing me. Hold - ing
Cadd2
C
Em7
Am
you; a feel - ing I nev - er out -
2.(See additional lyrics)
simile
Em7
A7-9
grew, though each and ev - 'ry part of me has
Dm
Dm(#7)
Dm7
tried, on - ly you can fill that space in -
3

G
Dm
G
side. So, there's no sense pre-tend - ing, my
mf
Dm
G
C
Em
Dm
Dm7
G
heart is not mend - ing. Just when I thought _ I was o - ver you, and
f
C
Am
Dm
G
just when I thought _ I could stand _ on my own, _ oh, ba -
C
Em
Dm
E7
_ by those mem - 'ries come crash - ing through; and I just

1.
Am
Dm7
Em7
Fmaj7
can't go on with - out
mp
C
G/B
Dm
you.
2. On my
f
Ped.
2.
on with - out; go on with -
out; it's just no good with - out
molto ritard.

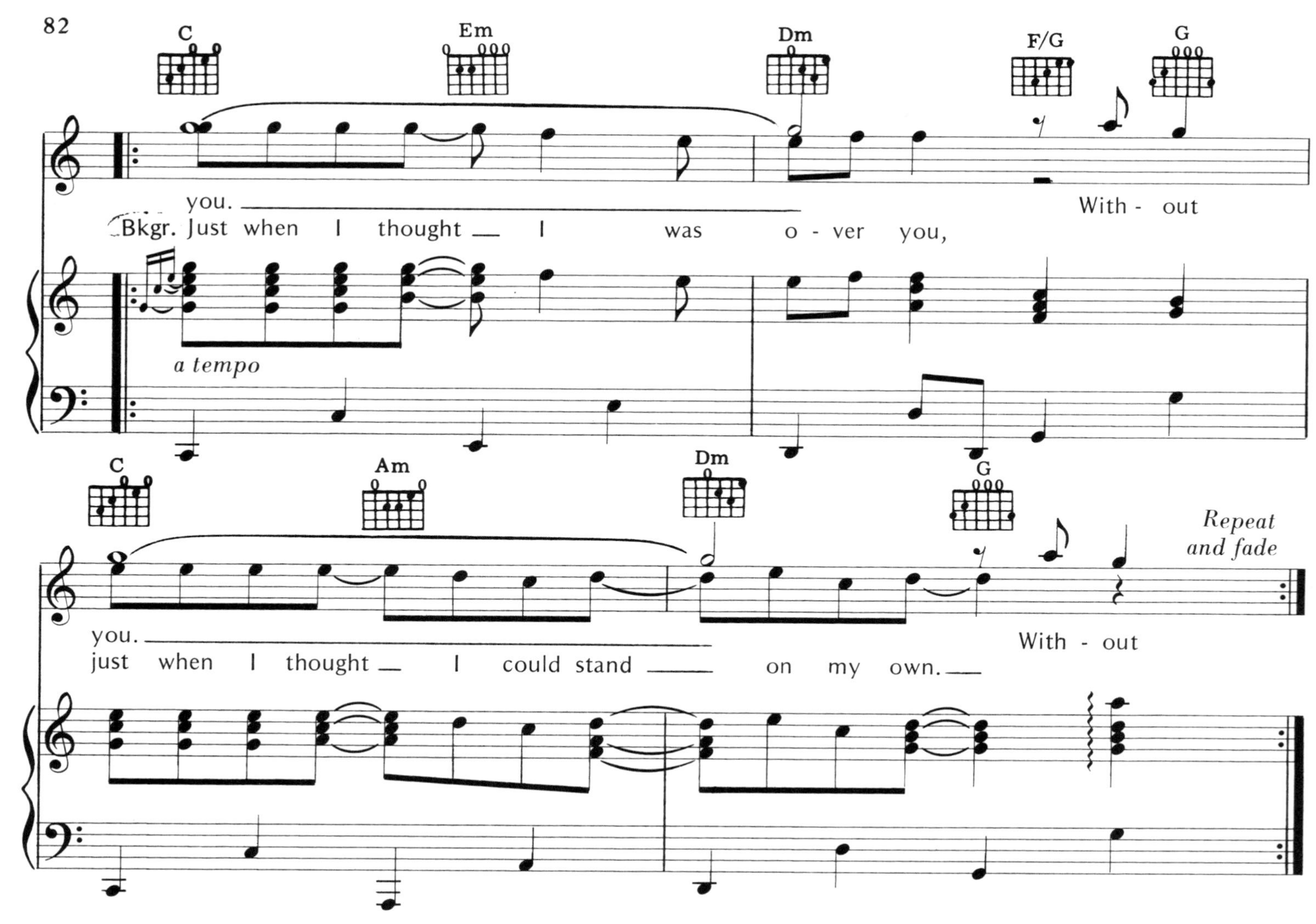

2. On my own;
I've tried to make the best of it alone.
I've done ev'rything I can to ease the pain,
But only you can stop the rain.
I just can't live without you;
I miss ev'rything about you.
Just when. . .

SWEET DREAMS

Words and Music by
GRAHAM RUSSELL

Moderate, with a steady beat
mp
gradual cresc.
ff
Dm
Am/C
1. This is the time when you need a friend; you
2. (See additional lyrics)
p

B♭
F
Dm
just need some - one near.
I'm not look - ing for - ward to the
Am/C
B♭
F
night I'll spend think - ing of you when you're not here.
Am
How ma - ny times will I think a - bout the things
mp
B♭
Am
I'd like to do?
Al -ways de - nied the right

Bb
— to live — my life — the way I want;
I want to share it with you. —
C
C/Bb
Chorus:
Dm
Close your eyes; — I want to
Piano Tacet 4th time
mf
f
C
Bb
C
ride the skies — in my sweet — dreams. —
Dm
C
Bb
Close your eyes; — I want to see you to-night — in my sweet — dreams. —

1.
F/C
G/B
B♭
D.S.
2.4.5. etc. fade
C
3.

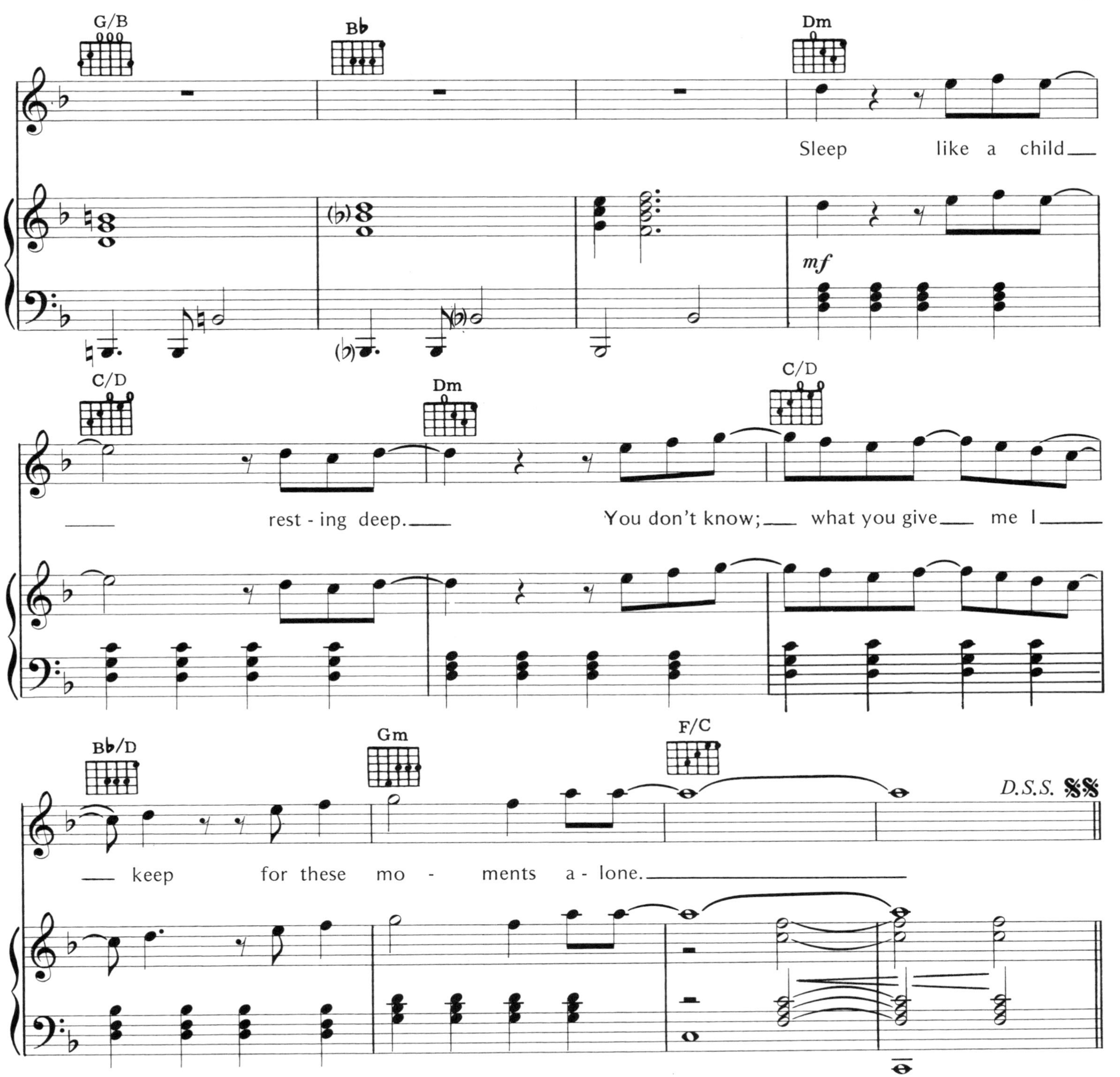

Verse 2: I'll think of your kiss as the day rolls by,
And I'll write the words you love;
And what I can't say in a letter
Will just have to wait till I get home.
Ooh, there's not much time to tell you
Half the things I should;
Only that I'm so glad I fell in love with you,
And I'd do it again if I could.

Chorus:

CHANCES

Words and Music by
GRAHAM RUSSELL

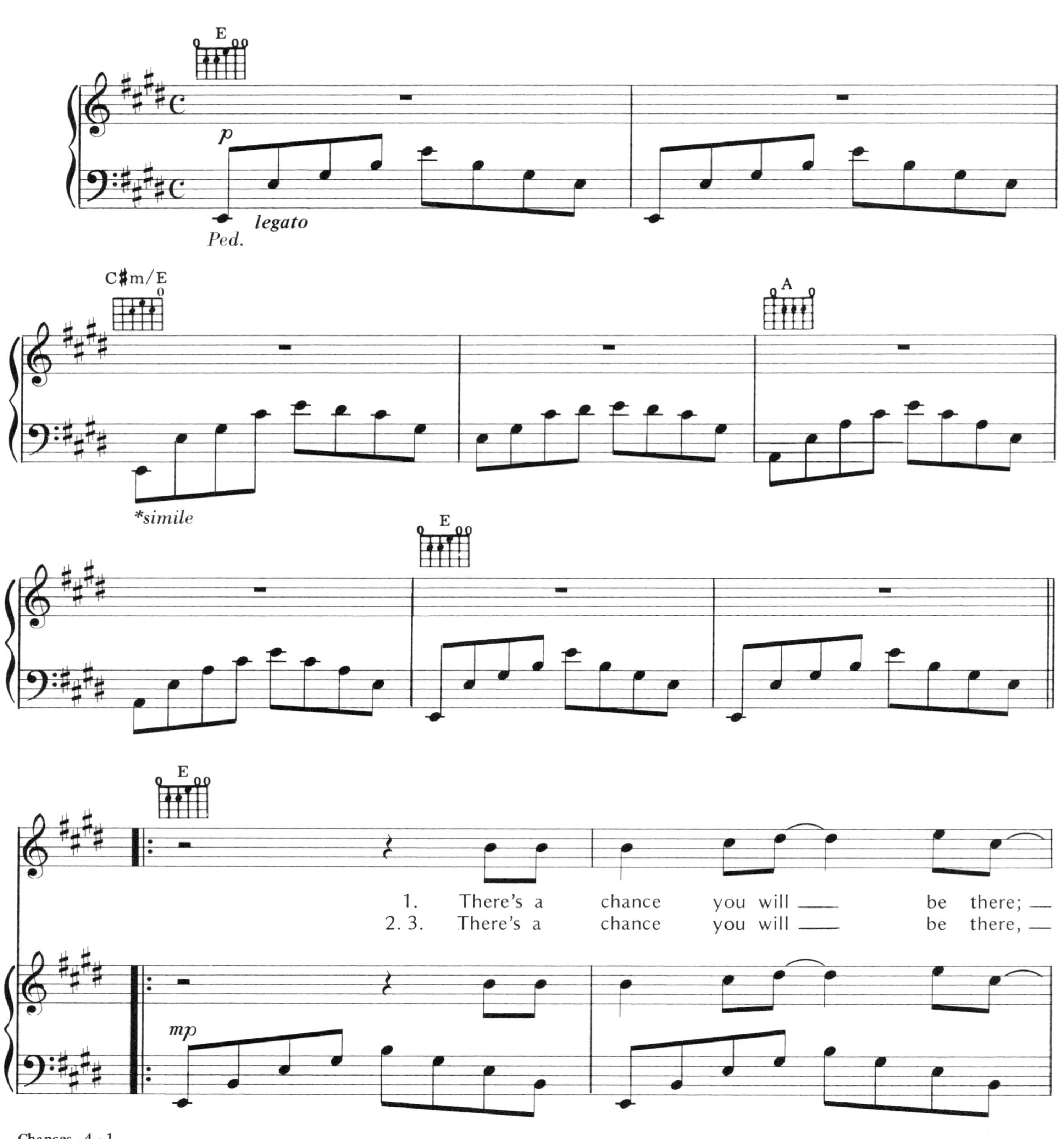
Slowly and Expressively
E
p
legato
Ped.
C♯m/E
A
*simile
E
E
1. There's a chance you will ___ be there; ___
2. 3. There's a chance you will ___ be there, ___
mp

C♯m/E
A
I'd like to know the truth. I'll
wond'-ring what to do;
B/A
find it out some - how; the chanc - es aren't too
how to play my role. I'll leave it up to
mf
E
C♯m/E
strong. A chance you will be there;
you. If I dis-guise my smile it
mp
A
please be there a - lone;
gives too much a - way;
help me speak of
and what if we can't

B/A
F♯m7
love.
speak,
Chanc - es aren't e - nough;
what then shall I say?
mf
f
A/E
one's too good to miss.
Don't you be too long,
Chanc - es aren't too
some - thing has gone
1.3.
A
E
strong; a chance is all there is.
(3rd time, end Solo)
mf
mp
Esus
E
Esus
E

2.

A E D.S.

wrong; the chanc - es are all gone.

(Instrumental Solo)

mf mp

4.

A E

wrong; the chanc - es are all gone.

mf f

B/D♯ C♯m E/B

R.H.

F♯m A/B B7 E

rit.

I WANT TO GIVE IT ALL

Lyric by GRAHAM RUSSELL

Music by REX GOH

E9/D
C♯7sus
I've come to see you smile. I
and hours just seem so few? With
C♯7
F♯m(add9)
F♯m/E
know you un-der-stand I have to say a-gain
days a-part so long it's hard to spend my time,
Dmaj7
B7sus
B7
E(add9)
it's on-ly for a-while.
when I'm so far from you.
And
E9/D
still you're al-ways here just wait-ing for my call.

C♯7sus
C♯7
F♯m(add9)
I wish I knew a way to
F♯m/E
Dmaj7
B7/D♯
give more than I do,
I want to give it all.
Bm
E9sus4
E9
A
Well, it
mf
A/C♯
D
E
does - n't hap - pen ev - 'ry - day,

A
A/C♯
D
but it hap-pened to me once be - fore.
E
A
A/C♯
Those ear - ly years I threw
D
E
F♯m
a - way, now I on - ly have to hear
F♯m/F
F♯m7/E
F♯m/D♯
your voice to make me feel so sure: that your
f
a tempo
mf

Bm
Esus
E
1. A
love is why I want to give it all.
B7/D♯
2. A
F♯7/A♯
That your love
Bm
Esus
E
F♯m
is why I want to give it all.
f
a tempo
F♯m7/E
D
D/E
A(add9)
rit.
p